50 FAMOUS
TANKS

by George Bradford and Len Morgan

A *Len Morgan* Book

ARCO PUBLISHING COMPANY, INC.,
219 Park Avenue South,
New York, N. Y., 10003

Published by Arco Publishing Company, Inc.
219 Park Avenue South, New York, N.Y. 10003

Second Edition, 1974

Library of Congress Catalog Card Number 74-80997
ISBN 0-668-01583-7

Printed in the United States of America

INTRODUCTION

This brief history outlines the development and use of one of the most intriguing machines of war. The tank was created to break the stalemate on the Western Front in World War I. Here was a vehicle able to negotiate shelled terrain, smash through barbed wire entanglements, cross sprawling trench systems and neutralize the machine guns which dominated battlefields. Once its impact had been felt, astute military observers realized the awesome machine was potentially a deadly weapon for fast, deep offensive thrusts. The Germans were the first to employ massed tank forces for this purpose and startled the world with their blitzkrieg victories early in World War II. Two views then existed as to the tank's proper role in battle. The British saw it as service and support for the foot soldier and evolved the infantry tank. The Germans equipped their Panzer divisions with light semi-tracked vehicles, freeing heavy tanks for independent operations against the enemy. Tanks and tank guns were tremendously improved during the second war, the vehicles of 1945 bearing little resemblance to prewar models. The vexing riddle facing every designer was how to build a machine large enough to bear a massive gun, stout enough to ward off armor piercing shells and yet light enough to cross rough ground. Larger guns called for larger turrets, more powerful engines, increased fuel supplies and, in turn, larger and heavier chassis. The turretless tank, or tank destroyer, as it became known, afforded mobility to a huge gun without having to bear the weight of a turret. While exceptionally well suited to defensive actions, this vehicle could be easily outmaneuvered by a conventional tank with a swiveling weapon when forced to fight in the open. As World War II progressed, the most successful designs proved to be those equipped with weapons able to pierce any enemy machine encountered and angled armor and cast turrets able to withstand frontal attack, yet light enough to enjoy full mobility. With the development of the anti-tank missile, capable of penetrating the heaviest armor plating, the role of the tank was drastically changed. It is now considered to be capable of offensive strikes only when accompanied by armored infantry carriers, self-propelled artillery and adequate ground support aircraft.

BRITISH / *Little Willie (1915)*

Little Willie with rear steering wheels. (Robert J. Icks)

It is only proper that a book about famous tanks should first mention the pioneering vehicle from which all others evolved. Designed by Sir William Tritton and constructed by Messrs William Foster and Company, "Little Willie" was demonstrated before King George V in late 1915. Built of boiler plate and entered through an access door in the rear, the twenty-eight ton machine crept along at three and a half miles an hour, steered by two heavy trailing wheels. Proposed armament consisted of two machine guns and a two-pounder, but weapons were never fitted to the prototype. Later, an improved model of rhomboidal design appeared and was known by the nicknames, "Mother," or, "Big Willie." Slow, clumsy and unreliable though it was, "Little Willie" was more than a hint of things to come.

5

2

BRITISH/*Tank Mk. I (1916)*

(H. J. Nowarra)

Early tests by British designers showed that a tank of rhomboidal profile possessed the hill-climbing and trench-crossing abilities required for operations on the battlefields of France. The Mark 1 became the first armored vehicle to enter production. The rear wheels were abandoned as internal steering was perfected. The "male" version was fitted with two side-mounted six-pounder naval guns while the accompaning "female" employed a brace of machine guns in each sponson to prevent its mate from being overwhelmed by enemy infantry. During the top secret development of the Mark 1, the curious were told the machine was a mobile "water tank" designed to supply exposed forward areas. To this day the term "tank" persists as the popular description of heavy armored tracked battle machines.

FRENCH / *Renault FT (1916)*

(Robert J. Icks)

Designed in 1916 and sent into battle in May, 1918, the Renault FT M17 was the most successful light tank of World War I. Weighing seven tons, it could travel five miles an hour for fifty miles, crossing trenches six feet wide. Its turret swung through 360 degrees and was fitted with a 37mm gun or 8mm machine gun. The Renault was supplied to French, Russian, Italian, Belgian, Polish and American units and served with several armies for many years following the Armistice. The tail piece supported the tank when crossing trenches and shell holes. The influence of this remarkable tank on a number of postwar vehicles is obvious. Two men made up the normal crew. With a total production of more than 4,000, the Renault was the most widely used armored vehicle of the period.

A later version of the Renault FT with formed turret. (WARPICS)

4

BRITISH/Med. A "Whippet" (1916)

(Robert J. Icks)

As World War I progressed, it became obvious that light armored vehicles equipped with machine guns would be valuable in exploiting breakthroughs made by heavier tanks. Sir William Tritton came up with "Tritton's Chaser," eventually known as the "Whippet," some two hundred of which were produced before the war's end. Two four-cylinder engines provided power, one driving each track, and a speed of about eight miles an hour was achieved. The "Whippet" was rather tricky to steer, however, as one throttle had to be retarded on turns. The slowed engine tended to stall during this procedure. Seven of these vehicles managed to overrun three German battalions south of Villers, Bretonneaux, in April, 1918. Except for local successes the "Whippet" had no great effect upon the outcome of the war.

(Robert J. Icks)

5

BRITISH/*Tank Mk. IV (1917)*

The many weaknesses of the Mark 1 led to the development of Marks II and III. Finally, with the Mark IV, the British overcame most of their early problems. Some 1,015 Mark IVs were built, far more than any other British World War I tank. The Mark IV featured improved cooling and ventilating systems to make crew life more bearable, hinged sponsons for easier rail shipment, unhitching beams fitted on top, a muffled exhaust and outside fuel tank. The previous boiler plate was replaced by armor able to resist the "K" type bullets now used against tanks by the Germans. The Mark IV saw action at Messines and Cambrai in 1917, demonstrating that the tank was a weapon to be reckoned with in future warfare. An improved model, the Mark V, was ready for duty by the war's end.

Mk. IV female with unhitching beam. (WARPICS)

GERMAN / A7V (1917)

Although by no means a successful design, the A7V was the only German armored vehicle able to stand up to the British tanks of World War I. This box-like machine featured sprung suspension, heavy armor and tracks copied from the American Holt caterpillar, all steps in the right direction. But the A7V had almost no ground clearance, poor trench crossing ability and was so tall it tipped over easily. Twenty were produced, three of which engaged several British Mark IVs in history's first tank versus tank battle on April 24, 1918. A powerful machine using two Daimler four-cylinder 100-horsepower engines, the A7V required no less than 18 crewmen. Normal armament was a 57mm gun mounted centrally and six side-mounted Maxim machine guns. Skirts protected the upper portions of the tank's tracks.

(H. J. Nowarra)

AMERICAN / *T3 "Christie" (1931)*

In the years following World War I, American tank designer J. Walter Christie invented a radically different suspension system for light armored vehicles. His machines were far ahead of their time in speed and maneuverability on rough terrain. While his novel ideas aroused little interest in American quarters, foreign observers were impressed. Of nine T3s built, two were purchased by Russia and copied for its BT series which eventually developed into the famed T34 of World War II. The United States Army bypassed the design and developed the T4 combat car in its stead. Christie's ideas influenced the British series of cruiser tanks. They are reflected in the large road wheels of the Crusader and Cromwell, successful tank designs of the 1940s.

T4 Combat Car.

13

FRENCH/*Renault R35 (1935)*

A replacement for the Renault FT, this eleven-ton vehicle was the standard French infantry tank when World War II began. The R35 was employed in large numbers during the Battle of France in 1940. It has a cast body and turret and was fitted with a short-barrelled 37mm gun and a single 7.5mm machine gun. Armor thickness varied from 20mm to 40mm. Eighty-six miles could be traversed at speeds up to twelve miles an hour. The two-man crew operated in cramped quarters and complained of inadequate vision. The R35 led to the Hotchkiss H35, a similar design enjoying lighter weight and improved mobility. The Hotchkiss rolled on six road wheels as compared to the R35's five, but employed the same scissor action suspension to be noted in these photographs.

GERMAN / *PzKpfw. II (1935)*

Although weighing but ten tons, this vehicle left its mark as the primary armored machine used in the German conquests of France and Poland. Its 20mm gun was outclassed by the weapons of most of its opponents. Rapidly replaced by the Panzerkampfwagen III, the PzKpfw. II carried on as a reconnaissance vehicle well into 1943. The main models, A, B and C, had increased armor and a flat front plate. Later models, F and J, produced through 1942, featured a prominent stowage bin attached to the rear of the turret. The PzKpfw. II saw considerable service with Rommel's Afrika Korps in the Western Desert. In highly modified form the Panzerkampfwagen II reappeared as the Lynx reconnaissance tank on the Western Front in 1944. A distance of 124 miles was covered at up to thirty miles an hour.

16

(Odell)

FRENCH/Char B1 bis (1936)

(Odell)

At the beginning of World War II about 500 of these 32-ton vehicles made up the main battle tank divisions of France. A 75mm gun was mounted in the front hull. The turret contained a 47mm low velocity A.T. gun and a 7.5mm machine gun. This vehicle incorporated such innovations as self-sealing fuel tanks, spring-loaded idler wheels, wireless, turret and floor escape hatches and skirting to protect the suspension. The crew enjoyed excellent vision in all directions. Both cast and rolled armor plate were used in the construction of this exceptional vehicle. This design influenced the design of the American M3 medium and British Churchill. A crew of four operated the machine for 140 miles between fuelings, covering ground as fast as eighteen miles an hour. This fine tank was outmaneuvered and unable to demonstrate its full potential.

19

GERMAN/PzKpfw. III (1937)

After France fell, German armored divisions were reorganized with this tank as the main offensive weapon. The original 37mm gun was replaced by the long-barrelled 50mm KwK L/60 on the J model. Model O was fitted with the low velocity 75mm gun and dubbed, "Sturmpanzer III." During 1941 and 1942 the PzKpfw. III and IV bore the main brunt of battle, the PzKpfw. III seeing extensive combat duty with Rommel in Africa. This tank featured torsion bar suspension and spacious quarters for its five-man crew. It was undergunned and eventually replaced by the PzKpfw. IV. Production ended in 1943 with 5,650 vehicles built, but the PzKpfw. III chassis was thereafter used as the carriage for several effective assault guns. The final 50mm gun used was capable of penetrating the American Sherman tank.

Pzkpfw. III/J, note escape hatch between tracks (WARPICS)/Opposite page: PzKpfw.III/L

143

BRAD/65

FRENCH/SOMUA S35 (1936)

(WARPICS)

One of the finest tanks of the day, the SOMUA is said to have been the inspiration behind the American M4 Sherman. About 500 of these vehicles saw service during the early days of World War II and gave an excellent account of themselves. This 20-ton cavalry tank was armed with a 47mm gun and coaxial machine gun. Its steel hull was completely cast and was 40mm thick. Power was supplied by a SOMUA V-8 gasoline engine which gave it a maximum road speed of 29 miles an hour. Vision was excellent from the commander's counter-rotating cupola atop the main turret. The crew of three was linked with voice tubes and telephones and afforded exceptional visibility through an elaborate system of episcopes and telescopic sights. German tank men held the French SOMUA in high regard.

BRITISH / *Matilda Mk. II (1939)*

Affectionately known to her crews as "Waltzing Matilda," this tank filled the gap in France and North Africa when British armor was critically under-gunned. The Matilda managed to absorb enemy fire until her two-pounder could be brought to bear, but her intricate design did not lend itself to mass production and the type was gradually replaced by the American M3 Grant and M4 Sherman. With armor of from 20mm to 78mm thickness and skirt-protected suspension, the Matilda could move along at fifteen miles an hour. This tank fought with success against the Italians at Sidi Barrani and Tobruk, helped stabilize the line of retreat at El Alamein in July, 1942, and was supplied under Lend-Lease to the Russians. In France in 1940 the Matilda took the best the Germans could offer and was responsible more than once in routing their advances.

Matilda II displaying the prominent side skirts. (WARPICS)

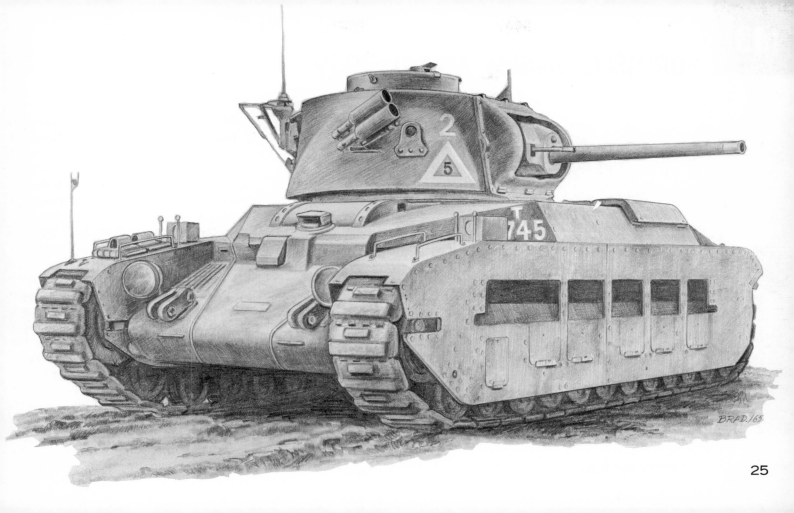

BRAD./65.

BRITISH/*Crusader (1938)*

Developed from such earlier tanks as the Cruiser Mk. IV (A13) and Cruiser Mk. V "Covenanter," the Crusader first saw action in the Western Desert in July, 1941. It was immediately apparent that the new tank was thin-skinned and undergunned with its two-pounder armament. A later version was fitted with a six-pounder and heavier armor attached but, during the critical period of Rommel's major actions, the Crusader had little more than its 27 mile an hour speed for protection. About 5,300 were built, the chassis of many being utilized as carriages for antiaircraft guns when the tank was withdrawn from service in 1943. British tankers, exploiting the tank's speed, became expert stalkers of enemy armored equipment. The Crusader was admired by its crews and respected by the Germans for its speed and maneuverability.

Crusader Mk. III with 6 pdr. gun.

Crusader Mk. I (WARPICS)

GERMAN / *PzKpfw. IV (1937)*

Closeup shows armor plate which was bolted to front and sides for added protection.

This tank was designed to supplement the PzKpfw. III as a support vehicle and was armed with the short 75mm gun for this role. By 1943 the shortcomings of the lighter PzKpfw. III had been fully realized and the improved PzKpfw. IV became the principal tank used by the Panzer divisions. About 8,500 were built in models A through J, production lasting until the termination of hostilities. With the invasion of England in mind, designers equipped the machine with a snorkel attachment permitting underwater operation. The short 75mm gun used in the early models was used with high explosive against anti-tank, artillery and machine gun positions. Not until the PzKpfw. IV had been refitted with the KwK40 L/48 gun did the vehicle become a true armor-piercing threat. Its five-man crew moved at 25 miles an hour.

BRITISH / *Valentine (1940)*

Vickers Armstrong, Ltd. completed development of the Valentine in 1939 and began production in 1940. The type remained in continuous service until early 1944, seeing much battle action with the British 1st and 8th Armies in the Western Desert. In spite of a number of minor defects, the type proved very popular with its crews. The original two-pounder was inadequate and was replaced by a six-pounder or 75mm gun. Although designed to support infantry, the Valentine was often pressed into service as a cruiser even though its top speed was only fifteen miles an hour. About 8,275 Valentines were built, including some 1,420 assembled in Canada, most of which were delivered to Russia under the terms of the Lend-Lease Agreement. A crew of three men operated the vehicle, with a range of about ninety miles.

AMERICAN / M3 "Stuart" (1941)

The first American light tank shipped to Egypt during World War II, the M2A4, was used only as a trainer. The improved M3 Stuart so delighted British tankers with its performance that they dubbed it the "Honey," a nickname that stuck in British circles. The Stuart saw its first desert action against the Germans at Sidi Rezeg, Libya, in late 1941. Once again the British found themselves with a fast but undergunned vehicle. Making good use of the Stuart's 36-mile-an-hour speed they often managed to surprise the enemy and bring its 37mm high velocity gun to bear with telling effect. The machine weighed twelve and a half tons and carried a crew of four. The side-mounted .30 Brownings were often removed to provide additional crew space. Its one point five inch armor was above standard.

M3A3 Stuart (WARPICS)

RUSSIAN/KV1 (1940)

This heavy tank appeared in 1940 and became an immediate thorn in the German side. It was overwhelmed, though due to superior training and tactics. Named for national hero, Klimenti Voroshilov, it embodied mechanical simplicity, good fire power, solid armor and lent itself to mass production with existing tools and labor. With the T34, it made up the backbone of Russian armor from 1940 to 1942 and became the basis for the Joseph Stalin line of heavy tanks. An odd feature was the turret's rear machine gun. The KV-1 was powered by a 12-cylinder diesel and equipped with a primitive but robust clutch and steering arrangement. The final production version was the KV 85 which appeared in 1943, fitted with the 85mm gun and turret of the T34/85.

(WARPICS)

GERMAN/*PzKpfw. 38(t) (1939)*

In March, 1939, Czechoslovakia came under German control and with it, the men and equipment of the Czech army. The Czech tank known as the TNHP was promptly renamed Panzerkampfwagen 38(t) and supplied to Panzer divisions. It was refitted with the German 37mm KwK L/45 weapon. Production of the vehicle eventually ran to about 1,200 machines. After 1942 it could no longer successfully fill the role of battle tank and was relegated to light reconnaissance duties. It also became the chassis for many German self-propelled guns, notably the Hetzer light tank destroyer. The PzKpfw. 38(t) saw service in Poland and France and during the early attacks against Russia. Weighing almost ten tons, the type could carry its four-man crew at 30 miles an hour and cover up to 150 miles between fuelings.

(WARPICS)

35

AMERICAN/M3 "Lee" (1941)

(Robert J. Icks)

In May, 1940, U. S. armored forces operated less than a thousand tanks, most of which were obsolete. The M3 began rolling off Chrysler's assembly lines in early 1941, utilizing many components of the M2A1. It mounted a 75mm gun in a sponson in the hull and a 37mm weapon in the turret. Early models had riveted hulls and cast turrets, later versions welded and cast hulls. About 5,000 M3 medium tanks had been delivered by the end of 1943 and the improved M4 was ready for production. The names, "Lee" and "Grant" were used, with "Grant" gaining popular recognition. The Grant used a British-designed turret and had a stunning effect on Rommel's armored attacks. Its great bulk made it an easy target for German 88mm anti-tank weapons, however. The M3 remained in limited service through 1944.

RUSSIAN / *T34/76 (1941)*

The T34 caught everyone by surprise in 1941, particularly the Germans. A vehicle designed for Russian winter conditions, it roamed the countryside at high speed while many of its opponents were helplessly bogged down. It featured wide tracks, a low silhouette and Christie-type suspension with large double road wheels. Its 76.2mm weapon dispatched anything the Germans then had on the front. The well-sloped armor and overhanging chassis which allowed a larger turret were ideas copied in later tank designs including the German Panther. The T34 was robust and of simple design, permitting rapid production. During the crucial Battle for Stalingrad, T34s were rushed into service without paint, so urgent was the need for armor. Armor thickness varied from 1.8 inches to 2.5 inches. Early models weighed 28 tons.

AMERICAN / M4 "Sherman" (1942)

M4 Sherman with cast hull (Musikoff)

The workhorse of American armored forces during World War II, the Sherman, became the best known tank of that period. Almost 50,000 were built. Early models saw service in North Africa where their 3-inch armor and 75mm gun gave them a decided edge over German equipment, particularly during the second battle of El Alamein. An extremely reliable vehicle, the Sherman weighed about 31 tons and could cover ground at 25 miles an hour. Numerous modifications appeared in later models involving suspension, chassis and engine. Shermans served as mine sweeping "flails," flamethrowers, rocket carriers, amphibious landing tanks and recovery vehicles. A good number were supplied to the Russian Army. Its main weapon was stabilized by hydro-electric gear to permit unwavering elevation during fire while moving.

(WARPICS)

AMERICAN / M5 "Stuart" (1942)

A direct descendent of the successful M3 Stuart, the M5 was heavier, faster and able to range almost twice the distance of its ancestor. The main differences included a fully-sloped glacis plate and raised deck to make room for the twin Cadillac V-8 powerplants. The M5 entered combat service at Casablanca during the 1942 Allied invasion of North Africa. It saw additional duty as a reconnaissance tank in France and Italy. M5s used in Normandy were fitted with an ingenious saw-toothed device designed to slash the rugged hedgerows of that region. While it weighed about 15 tons, it was even more versatile than the lighter M3. About 160 miles could be covered over roads and 100 miles under average battlefield conditions. The M5A1 was fitted with a 37mm gun stabilized in elevation, permitting accurate fire while rolling.

43

BRITISH / *Churchill (1942)*

Churchill Mk. I with the 3″ howitzer in the bow, and a 2 pounder gun in the turret.

Opposite page: Churchill Mk. VIII mounting a 95mm howitzer in the turret.

Below: Churchill VII with the 75mm gun.

The Churchill was one of the initial products of a crash production program begun in 1940, when the inadequacy of British armor became fully apparent. Early models were armed with the two-pounder gun, then the only available tank weapon. The Mark I carried, oddly enough, a 3-inch howitzer in the bow. The Mark III fired a new six-pounder and featured a redesigned turret. It appeared in 1942. Later Marks included improved features and eventually the 75mm gun became standard equipment. Churchills went into action at Dieppe with Canadian forces but had little opportunity to prove themselves as many of the landing barges were disabled before the tanks could unload. In the hilly country of Tunisia the Churchill proved itself an admirable armored vehicle. Its heavy armor was a welcome feature during the battle for northwest Europe.

GERMAN / PzKpfw. IV/H (1943)

With the introduction of the long-barrelled 75mm gun, the PzKpfw. IV once again took its rightful spot as an excellent armored vehicle. In March, 1943, the H model appeared with the elongated 75mm KwK L/48 gun, frontal armor plate of 80mm thickness and spaced armor aprons to protect the turret from hollow charge weapons. Massive side skirts were added and spare tracks carried on the bow plates. Additional improvements gave the J model of 1944-1945 reduced weight and better cross-country performance. During the war's final two years some 6,000 were produced. Although not as maneuverable as the American M4 or Russian T34, they could dispatch either of them and proved themselves to be tactically the most important German tanks of World War II.

1 BRITISH/Little Willie (1915)

2 BRITISH/Tank Mk. I (1916)

3 FRENCH/Renault FT (1916)

4 BRITISH/Med. A "Whippet" (1916)

5 BRITISH/Tank Mk. IV (1917)

11 GERMAN/PzKpfw. III (1937)

12 FRENCH/SOMUA S35 (1936)

13 BRITISH/Matilda Mk. II (1939)

14 BRITISH/Crusader (1938)

15 GERMAN/PzKpfw. IV (1937)

21 RUSSIAN/T34/76 (1941)

22 AMERICAN/M4 "Sherman" (1942)

23 AMERICAN/M5 "Stuart" (1942)

24 BRITISH/Churchill (1942)

25 GERMAN/PzKpfw. IV/H (1943)

31 GERMAN/JgPz. "Hetzer" (1944)

32 GERMAN/PzKpfw. VI "Tiger II" (1944)

33 GERMAN/Jagdpanther (1943)

34 RUSSIAN/T34/85 (1943)

35 RUSSIAN/SU85 (1943)

41 FRENCH/AMX13 (1952)

42 AMERICAN/M48A2 (1955)

43 RUSSIAN/T54/55 (1955)

44 RUSSIAN/T10 (1957)

45 AMERICAN/M60 (1959)

approximate introduction dates.

 6 GERMAN/A7V (1917)

 7 AMERICAN/T3 "Christie" (1931)

 8 FRENCH/Renault R35 (1935)

 9 GERMAN/PzKpfw. II (1935)

 10 FRENCH/Char B1 bis (1936)

 16 BRITISH/Valentine (1940)

 17 AMERICAN/M3 "Stuart" (1941)

 18 RUSSIAN/KV1 (1940)

 19 GERMAN/PzKpfw. 38(t) 1939

 20 AMERICAN/M3 "Lee" (1941)

 26 BRITISH/Cromwell (1943)

 27 GERMAN/PzKpfw. VI "Tiger I" (1942)

 28 GERMAN/PzKpfw. V "Panther" (1942)

 29 GERMAN/JgPz. "Elephant" (1943)

 30 RUSSIAN/JS II (1944)

 36 AMERICAN/M4A3E8 (1944)

 37 RUSSIAN/JS III (1945)

 38 BRITISH/Centurion (1947)

 39 AMERICAN/M41 (1950)

 40 AMERICAN/M47 "Patton" (1951)

 46 FRENCH/AMX30 (1963)

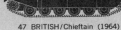 47 BRITISH/Chieftain (1964)

 48 GERMAN/Leopard (1964)

 49 SWEDISH/"S" Tank (1964)

 50 AMERICAN/Sheridan (1965)

BRITISH / *Cromwell (1943)*

One of the fastest World War II tanks, the 28-ton Cromwell was capable of 40 miles per hour and was the first British vehicle of all-welded construction. It featured the famous Christie suspension. Production began in early 1943 and the machine saw combat service in Normandy and throughout Northwest Europe. Power was supplied by a Rolls Royce 600-horsepower Meteor engine. Armament included a six-pounder and two Besa machine guns, one in the bow and the other coaxially mounted. The Marks IV, V and VII mounted a 75mm gun; the VI and VIII mounted the 95mm howitzer. Maximum armor thickness was 101mm on welded models. Speed was reduced to 32 miles per hour on later models to minimize wear and tear on the power plant and to increase suspension life.

Above: Cromwell VII with 75mm gun./Opposite page: Cromwell III with 6 pounder gun.

GERMAN/PzKpfw. VI "Tiger 1" (1942)

This tank evolved from standard German concepts, but incorporated vast improvements in armor, size and armament. It mounted the largest tank gun then available, the 88mm weapon, and featured interleaved road wheel suspension. It first saw action at Leningrad in 1942, but on terrain which denied maximum use of its long range fire power. Many Tigers in North Africa and Sicily in 1943 were abandoned when the enemy swept through those areas. The Henchel firm built 1,350 Tigers, eighteen of which were fitted with the 38cm rocket projector and called, "Sturmtigers." A 54-ton vehicle, the Tiger was equipped with underwater gear to permit fording where bridging was inadequate. Its weak point was its engine which required continuous maintenance. Two sets of tracks were provided, one for travel, one for combat.

Tiger I with spare tracks strategically located.

GERMAN/PzKpfw. V "Panther" (1942)

Considered by many experts to be the finest design of World War II, the Panther has excellent speed, mobility and climbing ability for its size (45 tons). Its 75mm gun could pierce anything in its class. It was the first German tank with a sloping glacis plate. Armor skirts were fitted to many Panthers as protection against anti-tank fire and "zimmerit" plaster applied to outer surfaces of hull and turret to counter infantry-placed magnetic charges. The Panther's 75mm KwK L/70 gun fired a conventional armor-piercing shell at a muzzle velocity of 3,068 feet per second, penetrating 5.6 inches of armor plate at 30 degrees from vertical at a range of 500 yards. The Sherman with its two-inch frontal armor was easy prey for a Panther from 2,000 yards range. Shermans built: 49,000; Panthers: 5,805.

GERMAN / JgPz. "Elephant" (1943)

This enormous vehicle was originally known as the "Ferdinand," being named for Ferdinand Porsche, its designer. With amazingly heavy 200mm frontal armor and a long-barrelled 88mm weapon, the 67-ton Elephant could only manage twelve and a half miles per hour on the road. Some ninety of them were ready for action in 1943 as "hunting" tanks. The first models did not mount a bow machine gun and during their first combat in Operation Citadel at Kursk they fell easy prey to Russian infantrymen who overran them and burned them out. Later versions were sent into battle with machine guns but the huge vehicle was never encountered in large numbers again. This machine was officially regarded as a tank destroyer because of its large gun mounted in a non-swiveling turret.

RUSSIAN / *JS II (1944)*

The first of the famous Joseph Stalin series of Russian vehicles. These machines improved on the KV chassis, the JS I being given a low profile and a hull overhanging its tracks to permit installation of a larger gun and turret. Its armor angled to a greater degree than the KV; its cast sculptured turret, eventually mounting a 122mm gun with long barrel overhang, gave it a massive appearance. Weight was held to 45 tons with modest exterior dimensions. Crew quarters were cramped and ammunition storage space limited. The JS II had a clean-sloped glacis plate, a more rounded turret and redesigned gun mounting. Some 2,225 were built by late 1944 and they saw service in many battles on the Eastern Front, including the final onslaught against Berlin.

Knocked out JS I (H. J. Nowarra)/Opposite page: JS II (C. Kliment)

ТАНК ИС-2

GERMAN / JgPz. "Hetzer" (1944)

When the German Army took over the Czech plants, it redesignated the TNHP tank as PzKpfw. 38(t). By late 1942 this machine had been outclassed as a fighting machine and was made the basis for many of the self-propelled guns required at the time. In 1943 an official request for a light tank destroyer on this chassis led to the development of the Hetzer (Baiter) and the entire plant facilities were soon devoted to this project. The Hetzer mounted the 75mm Pak 39/L/48 gun and featured a low silhouette and well sloped armor for all around protection. During 1944, 1,577 of these effective weapons were built. Hetzers were encountered in Western Europe and on the Russian front. Fitted with an improved engine, it was used by the Swiss Army after the war. In this peacetime role it was known as the PzJg.G13.

GERMAN / PzKpfw. VI "Tiger II" (1944)

While the Panther and Tiger I had balanced the Russian T34 threat by late 1942, plans were drawn to improve the Tiger by increasing armor and fitting the long-barrelled high velocity 88mm gun. The Tiger II, sometimes known as the "Royal Tiger," was the result. At 68 tons, it was the most powerful World War II tank. By March, 1945, 485 were in active service. Its KwK L/71 weapon could penetrate 200mm of homogenous armor at 1,000 yards, a considerable improvement over what the Tiger I could do. Its road wheels overlapped but were not interleaved (as on the Panther and Tiger I) and were not as prone to mud clogging. By the war's end even bigger and heavier tanks were under test in Germany including the mammoth 137-ton "E.100" and the almost unbelievably huge 185-ton "Maus." Neither saw battle duty.

GERMAN / *Jagdpanther (1943)*

Another of the many German attempts to utilize a standard tank chassis as the vehicle for a powerfully-gunned tank destroyer. The Jagdpanther with its clean sloping lines has long been a favorite of armor enthusiasts. It mounted the 88mm Pak 43/3 L/71, the weapon used so successfully on the Tiger II, and boasted armor plating 80mm thick. In combat the Jagdpanther challenged heavy enemy tanks from a concealed position and was almost invulnerable to frontal attack. Although restricted by its limited traverse, it was capable of destroying any Allied tank on the field. Its gun could penetrate 9.4 inches of steel at 100 yards at zero degrees inclination. With its low silhouette and great mobility, the Jagdpanther was extremely difficult to neutralize. It carried five men and could range for 130 miles on its fuel supply.

RUSSIAN / *T34/85 (1943)*

In late 1943 the Russians began replacing the T34 with the new 85mm-gunned T34/85. While the Russian weapon was similar in performance to the 88mm gun of the Tiger I, the T34/85 was not, on the whole, as potent a tank as the German Panther. The new Russian vehicle featured a much larger turret which made room for a five-man crew, but total weight was increased to 32 tons. Its gun could penetrate 4.7 inches of armor at 100 yards at zero degrees. After 1944 the T34/85 saw continuous war duty and was retained as a prime weapon into the 1950s. It is still employed in some satelite armies. This machine was supplied to the North Korean Army and was directly responsible for a number of American setbacks during the early stages of the Korean War. Few tanks have known such a long service life.

(Robert J. Icks)

RUSSIAN / *SU85 (1943)*

(Robert J. Icks)

Influenced by the designers of German turretless mobile assault guns, Russian tank builders came up with the SU85 tank destroyer in 1943. This heavily-armored vehicle was mounted on the famous and reliable T34 chassis. "SU" stands for Samokhodnaya Ustanovka, which may be translated to mean — self-propelled gun. In sacrificing traverse, the SU type permitted the installation of a much heavier weapon on a given chassis than would have been possible with a turreted version of the vehicle. The SU85 was in continuous action almost until the end of World War II, when the SU100 began leaving Russian assembly lines. The SU85 was a low, well-shaped machine of robust and simple construction which proved effective when used in battlefield conjunction with units of T34 tanks.

BRAD/66

AMERICAN / *M4A3E8 (1944)*

(Robert J. Icks)

This machine could be said to be the final practical refinement of the M4 series of tanks. Its improvements included a power traverse turret, a high velocity 76mm gun, horizontal suspension and wider tracks. While these brought total weight to 35 tons, the result was far superior to earlier M4 models. This Sherman entered battle in early 1945. Its rapidly-revolving turret enabled it to outmaneuver German Panthers in many instances. After the war it became the standard tank supplied to NATO nations and remained in service with some American tank units until 1955. Eventually replaced by the M46 Patton, the Sherman was recalled to battle duty during the Korean War when battle worthy tanks were urgently required to deal with T34/85s being sent against American units by the North Korean Army.

The Stalin III came as a surprise to the Allies when it paraded through Berlin as the war ended. Chassis and turret were of revolutionary design. Its elliptical turret and glacis plates sloped to insure maximum projectile deflection; it was amazingly low considering the monstrous 122mm gun it mounted; excellent mobility and a weight of 46 tons completed the picture. It is doubtful that this Russian ace-in-the-hole saw combat service, its purpose being to impress Western powers when the Soviets were anxious to exploit their war victories. Armament included a 12.7mm heavy machine gun atop the turret and a 7.6mm weapon firing coaxially from the gun mantle. Armor thickness in crucial areas was 200mm. This dramatic vehicle has only recently been retired from service in favor of the similar T10.

(Robert J. Icks)

BRITISH / *Centurion (1947)*

The Centurion appeared in 1945, just as the war ended. It featured a well-sloped glacis plate, large side skirts to protect its suspension and mounted a 17-pounder gun. The Mark II was exhibited in West Germany in 1949, incorporating an automatically stabilized gun platform which kept the weapon on target regardless of tank movement. Mark IIs were sent to Korea in 1950 and immediately proved themselves superior to their American M47 counterparts in fire power, reliability and performance. The Mark VIII was fitted with a 20-pounder and later Marks the standard NATO 105mm gun. Moving across rough ground, a Centurion has been known to fire 17 rounds a minute and score 100% hits on moving targets. It has served as the standard tank of Australia, Canada, Egypt, Sweden and Holland.

39

AMERICAN / M41 (1950)

(Robert J. Icks)

In 1943 the M24 "Chaffee" light tank put in its appearance and saw limited combat duty. This 75mm-gunned vehicle was the basis of the M41, a 76mm-gunned tank with improved chassis and turret. The M41 became standard equipment of reconnaissance and headquarters units and was, because of its 25-ton weight, air-transportable. When the North Korean Army began its push southward with its Russian T34/85s, American M41s were hurriedly flown in from Japan to provide infantry support. Although light, it filled the gap until M46s and M4A3E8 Shermans arrived on the scene. At that time the M41 was nicknamed the "Walker Bulldog" to honor the American commander in Korea. This type served with American and friendly army tank units.

AMERICAN / *M47 "Patton" (1951)*

Although a direct descendent of the M46, the Patton appeared with a completely redesigned turret and new controls and sighting equipment. Frontal armor was sloped for improved deflection and an improved 90mm gun installed. A comparatively heavy tank, the M47 displayed but average mobility, fire power and radius of action. After 1952 this tank came into general use with American units and with the armored forces of such NATO nations as Germany, Italy, Belgium, Japan, Greece and Turkey. It saw combat service in 1965, in Pakistan during the Indian-Pakistan dispute, and in 1967 in the Arab-Israeli war. The Patton's specifications include a speed of about 37 miles an hour, a loaded weight of 48 tons and a cruising range of 100 miles.

FRENCH / *AMX13 (1952)*

When the war ended, French tank designers came up with the 50-ton AMX 50 but the machine proved too expensive for mass production and too vulnerable in the light of new anti-tank weapons. They returned to their drawing boards seeking a light, mobile, well-gunned vehicle able to withstand hits by the most common projectiles. The AMX 13 was the result and it went into production in 1952. It mounts a 75mm gun but weighs less than 15 tons and should be considered a reconnaissance vehicle, or tank destroyer. An automatic loading mechanism eliminates the requirement for a gun loader. The engine is located in the front on the right side, alongside the driver's seat. The AMX 13 is sometimes fitted with launching racks for the SS11 anti-tank guided missile.

(Robert J. Icks)

AMERICAN/M48A2 (1955)

Introduced in 1953, the M48 is a further development of the M47 Patton, featuring a new elliptical hull and turret design to afford improved ballistic protection. The crew was reduced from five to four. Model M48A1 has a commander's cupola from which the air defense machine gun is operated. The fire control system has been improved to permit more rapid target engagement. The M48A2 appeared in 1955, featuring a fuel injection engine that increased cruising range and fuel cells of increased capacity. All of the Pattons mounted the 90mm gun with varied installations of muzzle brakes. The tanks that honor General George S. Patton, Jr., famed World War II American tank commander, have served with United States armored forces throughout the world.

An M48A1 "Patton"

(Robert J. Icks) 77

RUSSIAN/*T54/55 (1955)*

(Robert J. Icks)

The T34/85 was the last word in Russian tanks when World War II drew to a close. It was replaced, temporarily at least, by the T44 in 1945. The powerful T54 with its 100mm gun was by 1955 standard equipment with Soviet medium tank regiments, and with tank battalions supporting mechanized infantry units of the USSR. Once again, Russian designers came up with a heavily-gunned, well-proportioned vehicle of low profile and relatively modest weight. The T55 model includes such improvements as elimination of the anti-aircraft machine gun, addition of snorkel devices for underwater operation and conditioning to permit travel across ground contaminated by nuclear weapons. The T55 was first revealed to foreigners in 1961. The final improvement in this series is the T62, first shown in 1965.

After World War II, while Western powers were drastically reducing the size of their armed forces, Russian leaders continued to improve and re-equip their armored units. The JS III basic design was lengthened, a new set of road wheels added and its heavy gun improved. The result — the new T10 heavy tank. The most obvious external difference is the fume extractor on the T10's enormous weapon. The T10 was formally introduced in 1957 and immediately began replacing the JS III in heavy tank regiments of the Red Army. Although it is still known to be in service, observers believe the Soviets no longer emphasize heavy tank development and have stopped production of such machines. The British Chieftain, with its 120mm gun, alone can rival the T10's great size.

(Robert J. Icks)

45

AMERICAN / M60 (1959)

The M60 is currently the main battle tank of United States tank forces. It incorporates all of the best features of the earlier M48 but is powered by a diesel engine capable of greater range at a lower rate of fuel consumption. The standard NATO 105mm gun is fitted. Sighting has been improved by the installation of a coincidence range finder and articulated telescope. The commander's cupola is still evident, having been enlarged somewhat to enclose a short receiver .50 calibre machine gun. An improved version, the M60A1, features a turret and gun mantle improved contour, providing a lower silhouette and improved ballistic protection. The M60 is considered somewhat high and heavy for the size of its gun. American armored units began receiving this machine in 1960.

The M60A1 (Robert J. Icks)

FRENCH / *AMX30 (1963)*

This machine underwent evaluation tests in 1963 and has now become France's main battle tank. Its French-built 105mm gun fires a revolutionary roll-stabilized hollow-charge projectile, reported capable of penetrating 16 inches of armor plate almost regardless of range. A feature is its split-image range finder positioned on top of the turret and operated by the tank commander. This interesting 33-ton vehicle carries moderately heavy armor plate and depends upon its 40 mile an hour speed, extremely sloped armor and powerful gun for protection. The AMX30 can ford seven feet of water without special equipment, restarting its engine while submerged. "AMX" comes from Atelier d'Issy les Moulineaux, the name of the ordnance works developing French combat vehicles.

(Robert J. Icks)

BRITISH / *Chieftain (1964)*

This is Britain's latest main battle tank, a machine rivaled in fire power only by Russia's huge T10. It mounts a 120mm high velocity gun. Several interesting features are incorporated — a reclined driver's seat to reduce overall vehicle height and the use of bagged charges to eliminate the problem of disposing of empty shell cases being among them. A replacement for both the Centurion and the heavy Conqueror, the Chieftain, it is hoped, will keep Britain high on the list of tank forces. Turret armor is well sloped for maximum deflection of projectiles and provides an unusually low silhouette for a tank of this size. The new 120mm gun fitted to this vehicle can fire eight rounds a minute with amazing accuracy.

GERMAN/Leopard (1964)

This is the first all-German tank to appear since the end of World War II. It mounts the standard NATO 105mm gun sighted with a split view range finder which is operated by the gun layer. The Leopard is of distinctly low silhouette and flat turret profile and weighs a remarkably low 39 tons. Fitted with snorkel devices, it can wade through streams thirteen feet in depth, remain under water for indefinite periods and fire its weapon while submerged. Development of this machine began in 1961 and is now in full production, having replaced totally the large number of American-built M47s and M48s which made up a large part of the West German Armor since the fall of Germany in 1945.

(Robert J. Icks)

49

SWEDISH/"S" Tank (1964)

Early prototype of the "S" Tank. (Robert J. Icks)

This revolutionary tank design represents the new concept of the Swedish firm, A. B. Bofors, and is known simply as the "S." This is a turretless tank with a fixed 105mm automatic cannon. Gun laying is accomplished by elevating and/or traversing the entire vehicle by means of a special hydro-pneumatic suspension system. In use, the forward and rear running wheels are raised or depressed to elevate the main weapon. Twin machine guns are built into the sloping front and a third provided on the command cupola. A Rolls Royce multi-fuel engine powers normal movements while a small Volvo gas turbine provides extra boosts when required. The "S" tank provides enemy gunners with an extremely low target. This vehicle is proofed against atomic, bacteriological or chemical attack.

This recent American development is a 14.5-ton reconnaissance and assault vehicle designed for rapid transport by air. Constructed from a special light alloy which is heat-treated to provide good armor quality along with light weight, the Sheridan is fitted with the revolutionary new "Shillelagh" weapons system. Its 152mm gun launcher can handle the Shillelagh surface-to-surface guided missile and conventional rounds interchangeably. The vehicle is water-tight and proofed against the antici-pated battlefield threats of future war-fare. The M-551 has replaced the M41 light reconnaissance tank and M56 Scorpion 90mm self-propelled anti-tank weapon. Although small and light, the Sheridan boasts a fire power more potent than tanks several times its weight. It is certainly a tank of the future.

(Robert J. Icks)

RUSSIAN/T62 (1965)

The Russian T62 with its 115mm smooth-bore high velocity gun has been in full production for some years now and is gradually replacing the older T54/55 series. This is now Russia's number one main battle tank and its 115mm gun is exceeded only by the British Chieftain at the moment. This tank is readily recognizable by the long gun with cylindrical fume-extractor about two-thirds of the way along the barrel. The other recognition point is the spacing of the road wheels, with the first two close together and the rear three spaced out wider. The length of the hull has been increased by 25″ to allow for the larger ammunition carried. The turret has obviously been refined somewhat and the armor arrangement improved, giving this vehicle very clean lines. The West has never had to confront the T62, but the Israelis have, and have proven that any tank is only as good as its crew, as they have proven by knocking out numerous T62's during the Yom Kippur War.

The MBT-70 must be mentioned here, even though it was rejected as too expensive and sophisticated, and for the present has been shelved. This tank started as a joint project between Germany and the USA, with the hope that it would become operational by 1970. Its design was a major departure from conventional tanks and featured a hydropneumatic adjustable suspension which permits the vehicle to raise or lower its silhouette at will, and the driver position was located inside the turret with the other two crewmen. The most controversial feature of MBT-70 was its 152mm gun/launcher main armament firing both Shillelagh guided missiles as well as conventional spin-stabilized projectiles. A 12 cylinder, 1,475 hp diesel engine gave extensive range without refueling, and the multifuel engine could start, stop, and operate even while under water. MBT-70 could rapidly accelerate to 30 mph from a standing start and would have been more than a match for any tank in the world.

AMERICAN / MBT-70

AMERICAN / M60A2 (1973)

This tank is basically a standard M60 chassis mounting a highly sophisticated and revolutionary turret. It was hoped that MBT-70 would supersede it, but due to strong objections to the MBT-70 the M60A2 was permitted to evolve and is presently our top battle tank. The turret is equipped with an electrohydraulic stabilization system which inertially stabilizes the turret, cupola, main gun, and cupola mounted machine gun. Main armament consists of the 152mm gun/launcher firing both Shillelagh guided missile or the conventional round. A laser rangefinder for the conventional round is located above the gun mantlet, and infra-red and optical sights in an oval fitting alongside the gun are used for aiming and tracking the missile. The external configuration of the turret casting is unique, being designed on an in-line principle to provide greater ballistic protection. Its significantly reduced frontal area will make it less vulnerable to enemy fire. Ammunition stowage consists of 33 conventional rounds and 13 Shillelagh missiles, and secondary armament includes the standard M73 and M85 machine guns.

JAPANESE/STB-1

To date, Japan has never really produced an exceptional tank. However, with their new STB-1 scheduled to enter service in 1975 it appears that Japan has finally come up with a winner. This 38 ton tank has beautiful lines and reflects a cross between the Leopard and the T62, with a touch of AMX30 on the side. The main features include a hydropneumatic variable height suspension system such as MBT-70, which permits the vehicle to squat or rise at will. The main armament is a 105mm gun with an advanced fire control system which includes a laser rangefinder and ballistic computer, both developed in Japan. A semi-automatic loader automatically feeds the round to the gun, but is itself loaded by hand. The tank has a Mitsubishi 10ZF type 21WT V-type air-cooled diesel engine with an output of 750 hp. All in all a superb design and reports have it that a number of Western countries have shown an interest in it, particularly since the price is also most attractive.

89

GERMAN /Leopard 1A1

The Germans have always excelled in tank design, and once again they have produced a world acclaimed tank in the Leopard. Since its inception the Leopard has been continually improved and the latest improved model is known as the Leopard 1A1, with thicker frontal armor, a thermal shroud for the main gun, steel armor side aprons, new 2500 mile life tracks, and add-on stabilization. One step beyond this is the new 40.5 ton product improved Leopard 1A1 shown above with an early Leopard. This version features a new welded turret design utilizing the spaced armor principle, and will improve ballistic protection 100 per cent over the original Leopard. This improved model is already being introduced to German armor units. Also, at present a new and revolutionary Leopard 2(Kpz. 70) is being designed and tested, and from what little is known of it, it may well look like a very low-slung version of this advanced 1A1 shown here. Its main armament will be a German built 120mm smooth-bore gun with bagged charge, and a 1500 hp engine originally designed for the MBT-70 project.

DATA TABLES

	COUNTRY	VEHICLE	ARMAMENT	WEIGHT	SPEED	RANGE	CREW	Length	Width	Height
1	BRITAIN	Little Willie	1-2pdr. 2-MGs	28 tons	3.5 mph	—	—	26'6"	—	—
2	BRITAIN	Mark I(male)	2-6pdr. 4-MGs	28 t	3.7 mph	23 miles	8	26'5"	13'9"	8'1"
3	FRANCE	Renault FT	1-37mm or 1-MG	7 t	6 mph	15 mi	2	16'5"	5'9"	7'6"
4	BRITAIN	Med. Mk. A "Whippet"	4-MGs	14 t	8.3 mph	80 mi	3	20'0"	8'7"	9'0"
5	BRITAIN	Mark IV(male)	2-6pdr. 4-MGs	28 t	3.7 mph	35 mi	8	26'5"	13'6"	8'1"
6	GERMANY	PzKpfw. A7V	1-57mm 6-MGs	29.5 t	8 mph	50 mi	18	24'0"	10'0"	11'2"
7	U.S.A.	T3 "Christie"	1-37mm 1-MG	11 t	27 mph	150 mi	3	18'0"	7'4"	7'6"
8	FRANCE	Renault R35	1-37mm 1-MG	10.8 t	12 mph	86 mi	2	13'2"	6'2"	6'10"
9	GERMANY	PzKpfw. II/C	1-20mm 1-MG	10 t	30 mph	124 mi	3	15'3"	7'4"	6'6"
10	FRANCE	Char B1 bis	1-75mm 1-47mm 2-MGs	32 t	18 mph	140 mi	4	20'11"	8'2"	9'2"

	COUNTRY	VEHICLE	ARMAMENT	WEIGHT	SPEED	RANGE	CREW	Length	Width	Height
11	GERMANY	PzKpfw. III /J&L	1-50mm 2-MGs	22 tons	25 mph	124 miles	5	18'1"	9'8"	8'3"
12	FRANCE	SOMUA S35	1-47mm 1-MG	20 t	23 mph	161 mi	3	17'5"	6'10"	8'8"
13	BRITAIN	Inf. Mk. III "Matilda"	1-2pdr. 1-MG	26.5 t	15 mph	70 mi	4	18'5"	8'6"	8'0"
14	BRITAIN	Cruiser Mk. VI Crusader II	1-2pdr. 1-MG	19 t	26.5 mph	100 mi	4	19'8"	8'8"	7'6"
15	GERMANY	PzKpfw. IV/B	1-75mm 2-MGs	17.5 t	25 mph	124 mi	5	19'3"	9'4"	8'6"
16	BRITAIN	Inf. Mk. III "Valentine"	1-2pdr. 1-MG	16 t	15 mph	90 mi	3	17'9"	8'8"	7'6"
17	U.S.A.	M3 "Stuart"	1-37mm 2-MGs	12.5 t	36 mph	70 mi	4	14'11"	7'4"	8'3"
18	RUSSIA	KV I	1-76.2mm 3-MGs	52 t	22 mph	208 mi	5	22'0"	10'9"	9'0"
19	GERMANY	PzKpfw. 38(t)	1-37mm 2-MGs	9.7 t	30 mph	150 mi	4	16'5"	6'7"	8'0"
20	U.S.A.	M3 "Lee"	1-75mm 1-37mm 3-MGs	28.5 t	26 mph	144 mi	6	18'7"	9'0"	9'4"

	COUNTRY	VEHICLE	ARMAMENT	WEIGHT	SPEED	RANGE	CREW	Length	Width	Height
21	RUSSIA	T34/76	1-76.2mm 2-MGs	28 tons	33 mph	280 miles	4	19'10"	10'0"	8'0"
22	U.S.A.	M4 "Sherman"	1-75mm 2-MGs	31 t	25 mph	100 mi	5	19'6"	8'7"	9'0"
23	U.S.A.	M5 "Stuart"	1-37mm 2-MGs	15 t	40 mph	120 mi	4	14'76	7'4"	7'6"
24	BRITAIN	Inf. Mk. IV "Churchill VII"	1-75mm 2-MGs	40 t	13 mph	90 mi	5	24'5"	9'8"	9'0"
25	GERMANY	PzKpfw. IV/H	1-75mm 2-MGs	24.6 t	24 mph	124 mi	5	19'4"	10'8"	8'10"
26	BRITAIN	Cromwell VII	1-75mm 2-MGs	28 t	32 mph	165 mi	5	20'10"	10'0"	8'2"
27	GERMANY	PzKpfw. VI "Tiger I"	1-88mm 2-MGs	54 t	24 mph	62 mi	5	20'4"	12'3"	9'5"
28	GERMANY	PzKpfw. V "Panther"	1-75mm 2-MGs	44 t	28 mph	110 mi	5	22'7"	11'3"	9'10"
29	GERMANY	JgPz. Tiger (P) "Elephant"	1-88mm	67 t	12.5 mph	93 mi	6	22'4"	11'3"	9'9"
30	RUSSIA	JS I & II	1-122mm 3-MGs	45 t	20 mph	—	4	22'6"	10'3"	9'0"

	COUNTRY	VEHICLE	ARMAMENT	WEIGHT	SPEED	RANGE	CREW	Length	Width	Height
31	GERMANY	JgPz. 38(t) "Hetzer"	1-75mm 1-MG	15.8 tons	25 mph	111 mi	4	16'0"	8'8"	6'11"
32	GERMANY	PzKpfw. VI "Tiger II"	1-88mm 2-MGs	68.6 t	24 mph	68 mi	5	23'10"	12'4"	10'2"
33	GERMANY	JgPz. V "Jagdpanther"	1-88mm 1-MG	44.8 t	28 mph	130 mi	5	22'7"	10'9"	8'11"
34	RUSSIA	T34/85	1-85mm 2-MGs	32 t	33 mph	250 mi	4-5	20'3"	9'10"	9'0"
35	RUSSIA	SU85	1-85mm	29.6 t	35 mph	186 mi	4	19'5"	9'10"	8'4"
36	U.S.A.	M4A3E8 "Sherman"	1-76mm 2-MGs	35 t	26 mph	100 mi	5	19'4"	9'9"	9'10"
37	RUSSIA	JS III	1-122mm 2-MGs	46 t	23 mph	—	4	21'10"	10'0"	8'0"
38	BRITAIN	Centurion X	1-105mm 2-MGs	50 t	21 mph	150 mi	4	24'10"	11'0"	9'8"
39	U.S.A.	M41	1-76mm 2-MGs	25.5 t	40 mph	120 mi	4	18'4"	10'8"	9'4"
40	U.S.A.	M47 "Patton"	1-90mm 3-MGs	48 t	37 mph	100 mi	5	20'10"	11'6"	9'8"

	COUNTRY	VEHICLE	ARMAMENT	WEIGHT	SPEED	RANGE	CREW	Length	Width	Height
1	FRANCE	AMX13	1-75mm 1-MG	15 tons	43 mph	—	3	16'0"	8'2"	7'3"
2	U.S.A.	M48A2 "Patton"	1-90mm 2-MGs	49.5 t	32 mph	160 miles	4	22'10"	11'11"	9'10"
3	RUSSIA	T54/55	1-100mm 3-MGs	36 t	31 mph	215 mi	4	21'0"	10'9"	7'11"
4	RUSSIA	T10	1-122mm 2-MGs	50 t	26 mph	160 mi	4	25'2"	10'10"	7'11"
5	U.S.A.	M60	1-105mm 2-MGs	51 t	30 mph	310 mi	4	22'10"	12'0"	10'6"
6	FRANCE	AMX 30	1-105mm 2-MGs	33 t	40 mph	250 mi	4	21'11"	10'3"	7'6"
7	BRITAIN	Chieftain	1-120mm 2-MGs	50 t	25 mph	310 mi	4	25'1"	11'6"	9'0"
8	GERMANY	Leopard	1-105mm 1-MG	39 t	42 mph	350 mi	4	22'0"	10'8"	7'10"
9	SWEDEN	"S" Tank	1-105mm 3-MGs	37 t	31 mph	—	3	22'7"	10'9"	6'3"
10	U.S.A.	XM551 "Sheridan"	1-152mm 2-MGs	16 t	35 mph	322 mi	4	22'10"	9'2"	8'11"

WHAT FUTURE HAS THE TANK?

Until the end of World War II the tank was the most dreaded of surface weapons. Since then a multitude of anti-tank devices has been perfected, ranging from infantry-operated missiles to recoiless rifles, and these have been given much publicity. One is led to wonder if the tank has any future. Can it still play a successful role in battle? Obviously, no tank can be armored to withstand the punishment inflicted by these new weapons. In noting this, it should be remembered that almost every tank in history eventually faced a weapon which, when it was employed to full effect, destroyed it. The main idea behind a tank force is to neutralize the enemy's tank force. A tank must be able to withstand enemy tank fire and return it in kind. So, as long as a potential enemy maintains armored vehicles, we must develop similar vehicles to counter them. The requirement for a cavalry-like battlefield contingent remains, be it horse, tank or some vehicle yet to be developed which can exploit a breakthrough in enemy lines and accomplish rapid advances without regard to light resistance. An armored vehicle can function effectively in areas exposed to nuclear radiation, areas lethal to unprotected troops. Unless caught directly beneath a nuclear explosion, a tank's thick skin and modern protective devices keep it operating able to occupy and hold the nuclear battlefield until occupation units arrive. A recent invention which promises to affect future armored warfare is the hovercraft a unique machine which generates a cushion of air and rides upon it across land and water. Current versions are unable to carry significant armor but development of the idea may well see machines carrying light alloy armor and powerful missile-launching weapons maneuvering rapidly across terrain forbidden to heavy tracked machines. And if a tank can hover, perhaps it can fly. Who can compare struggling, awkward Little Willie with such handsome and deadly brutes as Chieftain and Leopard and say it cannot be done? Who can survey the long history of war from crossbow to nuclear bomb and say that anything is impossible? One thing seems certain — that as long as men wage war armored vehicles of some variety will support ground action.